D1402524

LADIES & GENTLEMEN

SIMON AND SCHUSTER · NEW YORK · 1951

Of the drawings in this book, the 225 identified below by their captions or a description were published originally in *The New Yorker* and copyrighted in the respective years shown by The New Yorker Magazine, Inc. (formerly The F-R. Pub. Corp.):

1926—"*The hussy . . .*"; "*There! That janitor's . . .*"; "*Lordy! Better'n a horse . . .*"; 1927—Decoration; "*Whoops!*" "*What's up, dearie? . . .*"; 1928—"*You're so kind . . .*"; "*I was discussing the Mexican situation . . .*"; "*Searle, come quickly . . .*"; "*Boo! . . .*"; "*Feelthy pictures?*" 1929—"*We want to report . . .*"; "*I say, Parker . . .*"; "*That's me.*"; "*Have you read . . . lately?*"; "*By God, Dinsmore! . . .*"; "*—and I consider . . .*"; "*By God, suh . . .*"; "*No, I can't . . .*"; 1930—"*Er—is that you, . . .*"; "*May I?*"; "*Let's not lose . . .*"; 1931—"*This is going too far . . .*"; "*Watch it, Major! . . .*"; "*What! No White Rock?*"; 1933—"*Tallyho, . . .*"; 1934—"*My God! Indians!*"; 1935—"*And that's the mater . . .*"; "*Why Alfred . . .*"; "*Whose little husband . . .*"; "*O.K. Cut her hard!*" Dalmatians; 1936—"*Come on . . . hiss Truman.*"; "*When you come right down to it . . .*"; "*Now we're going to keep on . . .*"; "*. . . Hello, Edmund . . .*"; 1937—"*I'm not supposed . . . Research Bulletins!*"; "*Watch out, he bites!*"; "*Oh, Edgar . . .*"; "*One would think . . . nasty colds.*"; "*He's not ours . . .*"; "*No, thanks . . . drinking brandy*"; "*Mr. Stowe is . . .*"; "*We're right back . . .*"; "*In the interests of science . . .*"; "*We can dispense . . .*"; "*You're a mystic . . .*"; "*Armbruster here . . .*"; "*Er—please sir . . .*"; "*They think I'm God.*"; "*Mayn't I have special . . .*"; 1938—"*I told you we should . . .*"; "*Hey, Jack . . .*"; "*You might at least . . .*"; "*I don't care how many . . .*"; "*Out here Nature . . .*"; "*I hardly know how to say this . . .*"; "*Now don't expect too much . . .*"; "*Damn plucky of you, . . .*"; "*I still question whether . . .*"; "*It's Connover . . .*"; "*But, Professor . . .*"; "*Now you look at her . . .*"; "*Funny, I've been entertaining . . .*"; "*Er—haven't you forgotten something.*"; "*By Jove, I'd almost . . .*"; "*Shoes by I. Miller.*"; "*He told me there was . . .*"; "*I'm afraid as a kid star . . .*"; "*Now let me tell you . . .*"; "*Hannibal, suh . . .*"; "*And how long . . . drydock?*"; "*Dr. Emerson! Please!*"; "*General Lownesbury met . . .*"; 1939—"*Every time he gets up enough energy . . .*"; "*Well, that's how it is, men . . .*"; "*Would you like to go down . . .*"; "*He's just about your size . . .*"; "*My God, Plotz . . .*"; "*Do you want to hear a funny story?*"; "*So, Bittleman . . .*"; "*Now let's talk about you!*"; "*Feelthy Easter eggs?*"; "*I keep wanting . . . pedestal.*"; "*You never can tell what . . .*"; "*Please, Mr. Carstairs . . .*"; "*She has the best forehead . . .*"; "*I can't help what address . . .*"; "*First then: the bulk of my estate . . .*"; "*He always was a fool . . .*"; "*Well, what's the excuse this time?*"; "*Tell me about yourself . . .*"; "*Rufus, you ole . . .*"; "*Well, if you ever need us again . . .*"; "*She's an eighth of a beat off.*"; "*Take it, Andrew!*"; "*Keep it under your hat . . .*"; 1940—"*And what is the purpose . . .*"; "*I suppose that some of these . . .*"; "*Now that's enough . . .*"; "*Why, George Carter! . . .*"; "*Now read me the part again . . .*"; "*There's a burglar prowling . . .*"; "*Speaking for the directors of the hospital . . .*"; "*You the husband?*"; "*You boys know the rules . . .*"; "*Ixnay, Edith . . .*"; "*He had a very personal question . . .*"; "*Why, George, you old . . .*"; "*We'd better get started . . .*"; Lady with bursting seam; "*That's Q37 . . .*"; "*One at a time . . .*"; "*Do you have the same thing . . .*"; "*I'm Edmund J. Murchison . . .*"; "*You're making a grave mistake . . .*"; "*Maybe after this . . .*"; "*O.K., Mother . . .*"; 1941—"*You needn't wait, Benson . . .*"; Police horse; "*Well, he never exactly asked . . .*"; "*My name's O'Toole . . .*"; "*You realize, of course . . . dismissal.*"; "*Alfred, your mother and I . . .*"; "*There's someone answers . . .*"; "*Maw! . . .*"; "*Sergeant, this is Mr. J. Stanhope . . .*"; "*I understand Bechton . . .*"; "*O'Hallihan . . .*"; "*May I inquire why . . .*"; "*I'm giving you your last chance . . .*"; "*I tell you we haven't got . . .*"; "*It feels like it might . . .*"; "*Is that one?*" "*Well, back to the old . . .*"; "*If you're so hell-bent . . .*"; "*Be sure to notice . . .*"; "*The boys saw their . . .*"; "*Never mind the damned cake . . .*"; "*Of course, Madam, the effect . . .*"; "*But I don't have . . . sugar!*"; 1942—"*But where is all this . . .*"; "*Welcome home . . .*"; "*May we be excused . . .*"; "*I want to report a tornado.*"; "*That reminds me of a parable . . .*"; "*It's been delightful . . .*"; "*He can't remember his name . . .*"; 1943—Man in shower; "*Will this train . . .*"; "*Will that be all, sir?*"; "*Watch out . . . hand!*"; "*In case of an air raid . . .*"; "*Oh dear!*"; "*You mean the Three Bears . . .*"; "*Here's to dear old . . .*"; "*Now who shall say grace?*"; 1944—"*She's sort of a secretary . . .*"; "*Oh, Mrs. Fordyce . . .*"; "*What would I do . . .*"; Shaggy dog; "*Why it's Mrs. Courtney . . .*"; "*Please, sir . . . table!*"; "*Young woman, do you realize . . .*"; 1946—"*I ast you . . .*"; "*Ah well, the Lord . . .*"; "*This is Major Belknap . . .*"; "*He said he considered . . .*"; Television singer; "*The truth of the matter . . .*"; "*I'm new at this sort . . .*"; "*I hate to think . . .*"; "*Hang on, Sarah! . . .*"; "*Ah, M'sieu . . .*"; "*The big guy in front . . .*"; 1947—"*You have so . . .*"; "*But I can't!*"; "*We do sell them . . .*"; "*. . . and now he claims . . .*"; "*O.K. Charlie . . .*"; "*For God's sake, Hortense . . .*"; Bears; "*What ho, Murchison . . .*"; "*Did you ever have one . . .*"; "*Then the Lord spake . . .*"; "*Wardrobe mistress . . .*"; "*Well, you're certainly friendly . . .*"; "*Thou hast eyes . . .*"; "*She got it by going . . .*"; "*Which one? . . .*"; 1948—Butler lighting pudding; "*By George, the other railroads . . .*"; "*Don't you ever do anything . . .*"; "*I wonder . . . Kinsey?*"; "*You're unhappy, see? . . .*"; "*It's been a lovely evening . . .*"; "*Come in, come in . . .*"; "*Sneaking off to Schrafft's . . .*"; "*How many does it . . .*"; "*All of a sudden . . .*"; "*Well, there's your . . . academy.*"; "*I think it's only fair . . .*"; "*Charles! Douglas . . .*"; "*Well, by gad, Madam . . .*"; "*. . . and now in this next . . .*"; "*Well! Finally!*"; "*. . . and now speaking . . .*"; 1949—"*Valerie won't be . . .*"; "*Irma!*"; "*Edward! Thank heaven! . . .*"; "*You certainly know . . . Benson.*"; "*Every year at this time . . .*"; "*Fill 'er up.*"; "*I happen to be . . .*"; "*Thank you boys . . .*"; "*Why, Harry! . . .*"; "*Easy, now.*"; "*Why I can sing . . .*"; "*I beg your . . .*"; "*I very nearly married . . .*"; "*Well! We track . . .*"; "*Of course you realize . . . bank.*"; "*I'll be all right . . .*"; "*She wants . . . water.*"; 1951—"*Look, J.B. . . .*".

The 6 drawings identified below by their captions or a description are copyrighted in the respective years shown by Horace Liveright, Inc.:

1929—"*Have I ever told you . . .*"; "*Why Auntie . . .*"; "*Ah, Mrs. Witherspoon? . . .*"; 1930—"*Wake up, you mutt! . . .*"; "*Good God! I forgot . . .*"; "*You're married . . .*".

The 15 drawings identified below by their captions or a description are copyrighted in the respective years shown by Peter Arno:

1935—"*Doesn't this remind you . . .*"; "*I hope the old buzzard . . .*"; "*Young man! . . .*"; 1944—"*They're amazing!*"; "*Visiting hours . . .*"; "*Just a weeeeny . . .*"; "*Have you tried an oculist?*" 1949—Spring in the City; Nude; Judicial Ire; "*Remember, Mr. Kornheiser . . .*"; "*Intoxicating . . .*"; Madam; "*Of course they float . . .*"; "*All right, McGrath . . .*".

MANUFACTURED IN THE UNITED STATES OF AMERICA

BY AMERICAN BOOK–STRATFORD PRESS, INC., NEW YORK, N. Y.

To Harold Ross

FOREWORD

In a big collection like this, covering some twenty-five years of work, there are naturally a number of my earliest cartoons. For the most part they will be found in the opening sections of the book. I admit that, being among my first, they linger in my affections. Furthermore, with all their inadequacies of technique and draftsmanship, they form the background for what was to come later.

For a starter, as a curiosity, here is the first thing I was able to sell to a magazine—a most memorable occasion in my life, as you might imagine. It was one of a number of decorative spots made for *The New Yorker* when it began publication. I think it serves to show with what small acorns I planted my field:

Up to this time I had been drawing, both at school and for *The Yale Record*, in a rough, rugged style—heavy blacks and dramatic lighting, for I was a painter at heart, and the slick, polished pen-and-ink vogue of the era was not my dish of tea. But I had found no takers among the magazines. The technique was "too advanced," "too violent." After several years of no success at all, I decided it might be expedient to tone down the style, at least till I had a foot in the door. This wise decision was reached just as *The New Yorker* made its appearance—exactly on cue. I've since believed, without a moment's doubt, in the theory of predestination. There's never been a better piece of timing.

IT HAS BEEN suggested that I answer, in this foreword, some of the questions that come most frequently to a cartoonist. Or at least to me.

Number One is: "Which do you do first, the picture, or the caption?"

With the modern cartoon, unlike the chicken and the egg, there is only one answer. The idea comes first.

In the days of the old *Life*, *Puck*, and *Judge*, many an artist drew endless variations of his particular specialty—boy-and-girl, old-gentleman-and-small-boy, monkey-talking-to-giraffe—and then some bedeviled staffer would sit down and tack on whatever variation of stock joke, pun, or he-and-she dialogue he could think of. It was the period, too, of the illustrated poem or jingle. The days of Daumier, Gavarni, and the rest were over. Artists, with rare exceptions, were no longer expected to think.

Harold Ross, in starting *The New Yorker*, cast out the stale joke, the pun, the he-and-she formula; and before long these faithful old servants were dying everywhere else—or everywhere, perhaps, except in the rosy pages of the Hearst papers, where they continue to this day to do yeoman service. In their place there developed, primarily in *The New Yorker*, a humor related to everyday life; believable, based on carefully thought-out, integrated situations, with picture and caption interdependent. This interdependence was the most important element of such cartoons. The reader had to examine the picture before the joker in the caption made its point, or vice versa. The quick revelation of incongruity (actually, the sudden realization by the reader that he'd been hoodwinked) brought the laugh. Or at least we hoped it did.

Here are a couple of early examples that show what I mean:

"I told you we should have given them something for Christmas."

"*Every time he gets up enough energy he starts after me.*"

Question Number Two seems to be: "Where do you get all your ideas? Do they just come to you?"

The last thing they do, madam, is "just come." My ideas are produced with blood, sweat, brain-racking toil, the help of *The New Yorker* art staff, and the collaboration of keen-eyed undercover operatives. For the first few years I did think up most of my own situations. I had to. I was developing a style and a new kind of format, and there was no way anyone else could do it for me. But as time went on, and a distinct pattern for my work was set, it became easier for others to make contributions. By "others," I mean the scant handful of gifted idea-men (there are hordes of the other kind) who have grown up in the field during the past few years.

This system, I think, is as it should be. No man, after he has evolved several hundred variations on the few basic human themes, can be expected to keep it up indefinitely. Not entirely by himself, at any rate. He has a large job, alone, in continuing to improve and vary the style he has developed: the struggle to avoid easy stagnation (if he wants to avoid it) is endless. For ideas for the pictures, new minds and fresh slants become a necessity.

The ideal collaboration—and I've been fortunate enough to participate in several—consists of sitting down together, with lots of paper and pencils, and digging; staring into the microscope from all angles, till suddenly the elusive germ is spotted. And sometimes this is only the beginning. Often it takes days and weeks of patient tearing apart and rebuilding of an idea before the artist is ready to start work.

I can hear the well-meaning matron who started this discussion saying incredulously, "What! All that fuss over a joke? Why do you go to so much trouble?"

There are times when *I* wonder why.

Money, I guess.

On the next two pages, for illustration of the foregoing, are an Arno idea and a contributed idea. Do you want to guess which is which?

"And what is the purpose of your visit?"

"Wake up, you mutt! We're getting married today."

The one opposite was a contributed idea; the one above was one of mine.

Question Number Three, from the more initiated, is likely to be: "Didn't you invent the one-line caption?"

I like to think that I did, and have been given credit for it; but nothing so basically simple could be "invented." It must be as old as Confucius, or older. It was lying there all the time, waiting to be picked up. I gravitated toward it naturally, and was one of the first to use it consistently, so that it became more or less a trade-mark. (Now, of course, it is found everywhere.) I suppose it appealed to me particularly because my English grandfather, who was the light of my boyhood years, had taught me that brevity was the soul of wit—a surprising maxim to come from a lifelong reader of *Punch*. As with a smoking-room story, the shortest caption, if it hits with a wallop, brings the loudest guffaw; the kind that warms my heart. The one-line caption or "overheard remark," together with its running-mate, the captionless drawing or "sight-laugh," would seem to be as far as graphic humor can go. I don't know. I admit I have been wondering for some time what the next step might be. (I may open some magazine tomorrow or the day after and find out.)

Here is an early drawing with a one-line caption, as well as one that needed no caption:

"Have I ever told you about my operation?"

I am sometimes asked, by those who remember them, "Why don't you revive the Whoops Sisters?"

(For the benefit of those who came in late, the Sisters were two raucous harridans, usually suspected of being deep in gin, who cavorted about town yelling "Whoops," followed by appropriate remarks, at the pop of the nearest button. Readers either grew quite fond of them, or were outraged by their language and general carryings-on.)

This question is an easy one to answer. I don't think the Whoops Sisters would fit this day and age. They came to me at the time they were most needed, both by me and by *The New Yorker*, and after running several years, they had served their purpose. By then I was able to handle the "big" pictures I'd been eager to do, so I quietly interred them, before I or others could grow tired of them. But they were fun while I was doing them, and I sometimes shed a nostalgic tear for them.

For club members who may feel the same way, I've dug them up again for a brief glimpse, and here they are:

"Whoops!"
"What's up, dearie?"
"Oh, nuthin' — only it's kinda nice t' get yer boots off fer a minute, now that th' fleet's gone—Gor!"

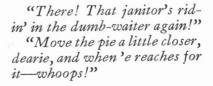

"The hussy—she says 'I'll give yuh a ring'—then she asks me 'is yer phone number under yer own name?' Lordy!"

"Whoops! Wha' did she think it was under—yer bust measure?"

"There! That janitor's ridin' in the dumb-waiter again!"

"Move the pie a little closer, dearie, and when 'e reaches for it—whoops!"

"Lordy! Better'n a horse and cab any day, I say! Get's y' there quick—hic!"

"Whoops! Where wuz you goin', dearie?"

One last question: "How do you go about drawing one of your pictures?" If you're an artist, the following will bore the life out of you, so skip it.

As briefly as I can describe it—and I think the procedure is fairly general practice, though naturally I speak only for myself—it goes like this. When I decide an idea is promising, I make a sketch in some such easy medium as charcoal. A "rough" of this sort takes anywhere from five minutes to half an hour, and while the idea is still fresh I try to cram into this first draft as much of facial expression and characterization as I can. I often hit it right, the way it's going to stay, on my first try. Background and details, except for sketchy indications, wait until later.

Sketches like this are gone over, at *The New Yorker*, at a weekly art meeting. The ones that seem funny and solid enough (there are always a few duds mixed in) are picked out for finishing, often with constructive suggestions for improving the picture or rewording the caption. Sometimes there are half-a-dozen versions made, over a period of weeks, on the same idea, before the thing feels right. Then the rough is back on the drawing-table, ready to go.

It happens that I work sporadically, in concentrated doses, so I get set now for a twenty-four- or thirty-six-hour session, in which I'll hope to turn out four or five finished pictures.

Occasionally a drawing, one of the simpler ones, comes off like a charm, and I'm finished with it in an hour or two. This brings a wonderful elation. More often, in the early stages, it's a long, tough grind, with endless penciling, erasing, rectifying, to recapture the effect and mood produced in the original rough. This penciling is the invisible framework that's later erased so the viewer will never suspect it was there—the labor and sweat which enable it to look as if no labor or sweat had been spent on it.

Sometimes this pencil layout won't come right, no matter how I wrestle with it. It lacks the life and movement it should have. When this happens I start all over again on a new piece of gleaming white board. Sometimes I make five and six beginnings, reworking faces and postures, striving for the exact comic quality the idea calls for.

But finally I think I've hit it, and am ready to continue.

Now you—let's suppose, here, that you're the artist—you dip a fine-pointed sable brush into India ink and start laying in the heavy black strokes that will be the skeleton of your drawing. You keep the line rough, jagged, spontaneous-looking. That's your god (or mine): spontaneity. You move fast, with immense nervous tension, encouraging the accidentals that will add flavor to the finished drawing.

When the ink is dry, if it still looks right to you, you start that awfullest of chores, the erasing of the maze of penciling that lies beneath the ink, till nothing is left on the board but crisp, clean black-and-white.

Now, with the skeleton completed, and the penciling cleaned up, comes the dessert course, the laying-on of the wash. (Rather an ecclesiastical-sounding process, I've always thought.)

The drudgery is over, the framework is up. You pick out a fat red-sable brush, the kind that used to cost six dollars and today costs seventy-five, and dip it into one of the washes you've mixed. All you have to do now is swim luxuriously in rich grays, startling blacks, and brilliant whites, while you build up the lighting effects that will make your characters stand out like actors on a stage—or so you hope. (To tell the truth, before I reach this stage I seldom have more than a general idea of what these lighting effects are going to be. Sometimes, in the middle of things, I find I've unconsciously switched the imaginary light source from the left side to the right, or from behind the characters to in front of them, seeking, without thinking, for a better effect. What I've done up to then, of course, has to be changed to coincide. This sometimes turns into a revolting mess.)

All of this, the inking and the laying-on of washes, must be done rapidly, with careless care, so that it doesn't look like work. It must look fast and loose, with a drawn-on-the spot quality. If you decide finally that, despite all your efforts, it's come out too slick, too finished, too static—boom! Over you start again, and far into the night. . . .

But if finally, at long last, you're sure you've hit it, so that it looks as right to you as you can make it, you set it up in front of a deep armchair and settle back to look at it, even though dawn is breaking in the street outside and your eyes are burning in your head with fatigue; and you gaze on it with a loving joy, and you say to yourself, with a bit of surprise, "By golly, I made it!"

PETER ARNO

New York City
September, 1951

LADIES & GENTLEMEN

"You're so kind to me, and I'm so tired of it all!"

"I was discussing the Mexican situation with Bottomley today.
It seems fraught with interest."

"*Searle, come quickly. The soap has floated out of reach!*"

"Doesn't this remind you of Lake Geneva?"

"This is going too far, Remson! Someone's purloined my Burberry!"

"Good God! I forgot to get favors for the men!"

"Why Auntie—what big eyes you have!"

"Er—is that you, Gwendolyn? I believe this is our
dance, Gwendolyn."

"We want to report a stolen car."

"*I say, Parker—there seems to be a gull in the study.*"

"And that's the mater, God bless her and all that sort of thing."

"Boo! You pretty creature!"

"*I hope the old buzzard turns west on 57th!*"

"My God! Indians!"

"*Young man! You put that celery in a bag, where it belongs!*"

"Why Alfred! Your hands are like ice!"

"That's me."

"*Come on—we're going to the Trans-Lux and hiss Truman.*"

"Have you read any good books lately?"

"By God, Dinsmore! Were you staring at my wife's ankles?"

"—and I consider your conduct unethical and lousy."

"Ah, Mrs. Witherspoon? I represent—"

"Whose little husband are you?"

"By God, suh—Ah won't fohget this insult!"

"May I?"

"Watch it, Major! You caught me right
in the abdomen!"

"I suppose that some of these attachments eventually ripen into lasting friendships."

"Now that's enough! Run along!"

"Will this train take me anywhere near the Racquet Club?"

"*I'm not supposed to let anybody see my Consumers'*
Research Bulletins!"

"*Watch out, he bites!*"

"O.K. Cut her hard!"

"Tallyho, godammit!"

"No, I can't. I'm all worn out. If I weren't so tired I'd be attending
a funeral in Bay Ridge."

"They're amazing!"

"When you come right down to it, though, in what way is this any different from Kew Gardens?"

"You needn't wait, Benson. I'll be some time."

"Well, that's how it is, men. You just rub two dry sticks together."

"What! No White Rock?"

"You're married, aren't you?"

"Will that be all, sir?"

"Would you like to go down the Allagash with me in a canoe? It empties into the St. John."

"*Well, he never exactly asked me to marry him in so many words.*"

"*She's sort of a secretary. With the new tax setup, I figure she's only costing me eight cents on the dollar.*"

"Oh, Mrs. Fordyce—could I trouble you to come here for a moment?"

"Why, George Carter! What keeps *you* in town?"

"But where is all this leading us to, Mr. Hartman—Miami? Palm Beach? Hollywood?"

"Oh, Edgar—I never <u>dreamed</u> it would be like this!"

"Watch out for his free hand!"

"My name's O'Toole and any man in the house can lick me!"

"*Valerie won't be around for several days. She backed into a sizzling platter.*"

"Hey, Jack, which way to Mecca?"

"*Welcome home, Colonel Bagley, suh! Welcome home!*"

"Now read me the part again where I disinherit everybody."

"May we be excused for a few minutes, Mamma? I want to show Miss deWalden the new septic tank."

"*What would I do if I were General Eisenhower? I'll tell you what I'd do if I were General Eisenhower. I'd do exactly what General <u>Lee</u> would have done if <u>he'd</u> been General Eisenhower! <u>That's</u> what I'd do if I were General Eisenhower, suh!*"

"You have __so__ got it turned off!"

"Visiting hours are over, Mr. Kugelman."

Spring In The City

"But I can't!"

"There's a burglar prowling about in the Blue Room,
sir. Would you care to have a crack at him before I notify the police?"

"Irma! Go put some clothes on!"

"You might at least say 'Aloha,' dear."

"Edward! Thank heavens! I couldn't imagine __what__ had happened to you!"

"He's just about your size—damn it!"

"*Now we're going to keep on doing this over and over until whoever is yelling 'Whoopee' decides to co-operate.*"

"Easy now, men! Watch those itching fingers!"

"Let's not lose our tempers, sir!"

"You certainly know my Achilles' heel, Mr. Benson."

"My God, Plotz, I asked for Senators! SEN-A-TORS! Like in Washington!"

"Do you want to hear a funny story?"

"Every year at this time it's the same thing—he gets to brooding about the old Miss Rheingold."

"Feelthy pictures?"

"So, Bittleman! Our paths cross again!"

"*You realize, of course, Burton, that this means automatic dismissal.*"

Judicial Ire

"*We do sell them sometimes, lady, but only to other teams.*"

"I don't care how many are left over, Mrs. Ransome. I tell you I only brought one!"

"Out here Nature makes her own laws. You, Miss Marlowe,
are a woman and I am a man."

"Fill 'er up."

"Now let's talk about you!"

"*Alfred, your mother and I think it would be a good idea for you to knock about on your own for a while—just on the estate, of course.*"

"There's someone answers your description at the Morgue. Shall I say it isn't you?"

"By George, the other railroads certainly have a lot to learn from the Chesapeake and Ohio."

"*Speaking for the directors of the hospital, I would like to say, Mrs. Hart, that it was nice having you with us.*"

"Just a weeeeny bit lower, Miss Snodgrass."

"Feelthy Easter eggs?"

"... and now he claims diplomatic immunity."

"I hardly know how to say this, Mrs. Landecker, but what you've got there is pre-patellar bursitis, or—er—a bad case of housemaid's knee."

"O.K., Charlie. This is the place."

"You the husband?"

"*I happen to be a MacNab, Miss. I couldn't help noticing that you're wearing our tartan.*"

"Now don't expect too much. This is my first time on skates."

"For God's sake, Hortense, where are my elevator shoes?"

"You boys know the rules. No low blows, no hitting in the clinches, break clean, and at all times keep your pants up."

"*I want to report a tornado.*"

"Maw! Myrtle's back. Looks like she made good."

"That reminds me of a parable they were telling in Scranton, P-A."

"Damn plucky of you, Gillespie, fighting through like this."

"*Ixnay, Edith. I just found out we're at the wrong party.*"

"It's been delightful having you with us, Mrs. Parkhurst."

"In case of an air raid, Billings, what will be done about <u>us</u>?"

"*I keep wanting to put you on a pedestal.*"

"*Sergeant, this is Mr. J. Stanhope Alderson. He has money, position, many influential friends, and we can't do this to him.*"

"I understand Bechton was cashiered for grousing."

"He can't remember his name, Sergeant. All he remembers is he's somebody pretty damned important."

"He had a very personal question, Mr. Dexter."

"Oh dear!"

"One would think she'd be subject to a series of nasty colds."

"Have you tried an oculist?"

"You never can tell what they're thinking, can you?"

"Why, it's Mrs. Courtney Richardson, Senior—she's heading this way!"

"Please, sir—this isn't my table!"

"Please, Mr. Carstairs! Not here!"

"O'Hallihan, you know too much!"

"*May I inquire __why__ there is no more Château Lafite?*"

"Thank you, boys. I'll take it from here."

"... Hello, Edmund. Hello, Warwick. Hello, Teddy, Hello,
Poodgie. Hello, Freddie ..."

"*I still question whether this will be legally binding in New York State.*"

"*I'm giving you your last chance, Willis!
If your horse doesn't come in today, you're fired!*"

"*You mean the Three Bears raised all that stink over a lousy bowl of breakfast food?*"

"He's not ours. Try River House."

"*I tell you we haven't got any aluminum!*"

"Why, George, you old scoundrel! I'm glad to see you!"

"Why, Harry! You're shorter than I am!"

"It's Conover—Car 4—seventy-sixth floor. He's running blind in a fog!"

"Young woman, do you realize my time is worth thirty dollars a minute?"

"She has the best forehand drive in Liberia."

"Easy, now."

"*But, Professor, remember the thousands of little school children who gave their pennies to send us on this expedition.*"

"Here's to dear old Pomfret, drink 'er down, drink 'er down."

"I can't help what address you have. We are not a needy family."

"*It feels like it might be a grain of sand.*"

"First then: the bulk of my estate, excepting certain specific bequests as hereinafter noted, I leave to my true friend and companion, one of God's noblest creatures . . ."

"No, thanks. I've been drinking brandy."

"I ast you not to slam the door!"

"Ah well, the Lord giveth, and the Lord taketh away."

"*Mr. Stowe is on the terrace, Ma'am. He's—er—dropping hot pennies on the sidewalk.*"

"*Now you look at her with deep reverence. Then we pan out to the next scene, which will be in the maternity hospital.*"

"Why, *I* can sing better than *that!*"

"He always was a fool for a pretty face."

"I beg your pardon."

"I beg your pardon."

"Funny, I've been entertaining the same wild hope."

"Remember, Mr. Kornheiser—no patting it smooth this time."

"Well, what's the excuse this time?"

"Don't you ever do anything but covers for historical novels, Mr. Carmichael?"

"Tell me about yourself—your struggles, your dreams, your telephone number."

"Rufus, you ole black rascal, get me a vermouth cassis."

"*I very nearly married her once. Fortunately, I had a cracking good lawyer.*"

"*Well! We track that old 'possum to his lair, men?*"

"We'd better get started, dear. Time and tide, you know . . ."

"Er—haven't you forgotten something?"

"*Is that one?*"

"I wonder if there's a <u>Mrs.</u> Kinsey?"

"We're right back where we started. This is ordinary cow's milk."

"What ho, Murchison—did you bag him?"

"In the interests of science, Miss Mellish, I'm going to make a rather strange request of you."

"You're unhappy, see? You're an unwanted child. You were born out of wedlock."

"This is Major Belknap, dear. He hasn't seen a white woman in three years."

"We can dispense with those long low whistles, Mr. Fitch!"

"Now who shall say grace?"

"Well, back to the old drawing board."

"*Of course you realize this washes me up at the bank.*"

"By Jove, I'd almost dip into capital for her."

"Shoes by I. Miller."

"Intoxicating, isn't it?"

"*It's been a lovely evening, Mr. Voorhees. Please let's not spoil it.*"

"*He told me there was a storm coming up, so like a fool
I let him tie me to the mast.*"

"*That's Q37, in her day one of the most effective secret agents this country ever had.*"

"He said he considered our decision incompetent, delusive, and vin-dictive. Then he hung this mouse on me."

"Come in, come in, whoever you are."

"Well, if you ever need us again just give us a ring."

"*Did you ever have one of those awful days when everything just seems to go right?*"

"One at a time, dammit, one at a time!"

"*I'm afraid as a kid star he's through.*"

"Sneaking off to Schrafft's again, eh?"

"*The truth of the matter, gentlemen, is that Joan of Arc was quite flat-chested.*"

"You're a mystic, Mr. Ryan. <u>All</u> Irishmen are mystics."

"Then the Lord spake unto them, saying—and I quote . . ."

"If you're so hell-bent on buying something that belongs to Mr. Hearst, you can get a Journal-American for five cents."

"How many does it—er—sleep?"

"All of a sudden you stop saying 'we.'"

"Now let me tell you about my troubles!"

"*I'm new at this sort of thing. Just what points does one base one's decision on?*"

"She's an eighth of a beat off."

"*Wardrobe mistress would like a word with you, Miss Jackson.*"

"*Be sure to notice Mrs. Newbold when she gets up. She's wearing a really lovely gown.*"

"The boys saw their first skunk today."

"I hate to think of waking him. He didn't get in till all hours."

"*Armbruster here has what I think is a marvellous suggestion.*"

Madam

"I'll be all right in a few minutes. The people at the next table were drinking Scotch and 7-Up!"

"Never mind the damned cake! Where are the reporters?"

"*Of course, Madam, the effect would be a good deal different with the salt spray in his face and the wind whipping through his hair.*"

"Well, you're certainly friendly. Now, just what are the terms?"

"But I don't have a lump of sugar!"

"*She wants a drink of water.*"

"Hannibal, suh, the General Joseph E. Johnston of the Punic Wars."

"And how long, may I ask, have we been in drydock?"

"Er—please, sir. We mustn't interpret the word 'hostess' too broadly."

"Take it, Andrew!"

"*Keep it under your hat, but when this crowd thins out, I have some marshmallows.*"

"Thou hast eyes to see but seest not!"

"Well, there's your 'nearby military academy.'"

"Do you have the same thing in a cook?"

"Hang on, Sarah! Keep your place!"

"Dr. Emerson! Please!"

"Ah, M'sieu, I have a table for you now."

"I'm Edmund J. Murchison of 222 Morton Street! A horrible mistake has been made!"

"*I think it's only fair to tell you, Miss Parsons, that I'm a happily married man.*"

"Charles! Douglas Aircraft has alerted Theodora!"

"*The big guy in front is Joseph T. Cochrane. Call him Joe. You met him in Marysville three weeks ago. Talk about hunting. He goes after deer every fall. Man on left is Leo Brown. Sixteenth District in his pocket. Don't ask about his wife. She's ditched him. Fellow with mustache is Jim Cronin. Watch your step with him. He's Cochrane's brother-in-law, and . . .*"

"*You're making a grave mistake, Miss Loesch. We scoutmasters are not entrusted with military secrets.*"

"*Well, by gad, Madam, something nipped me!*"

"General Lownesbury met a strange end—felled by a Flexible Flyer."

"*Maybe after this you'll realize that when I say I'm going to dive, I mean it. Now go below and dry yourself.*"

"They think I'm God."

"... and now in this next scene you've graduated from medical school and become the most famous neuropathologist in the world."

"Of course they float. What did you think?"

"Well! Finally!"

"She got it by going 'br-r-r-r' in front of Bergdorf's."

"All right, McGrath—we know you're in there!"

"O.K., Mother. You can knock off for lunch."

"*Which one? Great heavens, are you mad?*"

"Mayn't I have special consideration? I'm the husband."

"... and now speaking confidentially—"

*"Look, J. B.—it turns out this Frietchie dame was
ninety goddam years old!"*